FRIENDSHIP
for kids

THE POWER, PURPOSE, AND
PROVISION OF FRIENDSHIP.

LOVEGODGREATLY.COM

A Word to Parents

This book grew out of a desire to
provide a companion study journal
for children to use alongside the
Friendship adult study journal and book.

Love God Greatly is dedicated to making
God's Word available to our beautiful
community of women... and now, women
have the opportunity to share God's Word
with children through this study uniquely
crafted for young hearts.

CONTENTS

INTRODUCTION
FRIENDSHIP

Did you know Jesus prayed for you? His prayer for you was for you to be unified with other believers in Christ. When you love and are unified with other believers in Christ you show the world God's love.

God loved the world so much He sent His only Son to die for our sins. When Jesus died for our sins, He showed the world God's love. Jesus' sacrifice showed everyone how much He loved us and considered us His friends. John 15:13 says, "No one has greater love than this—that one lays down his life for his friends." Jesus' sacrifice was the ultimate example of loving friendship. He loved us so much He died so we could live with Him forever.

God created us to have friendships. God wanted us to not only have a relationship with Him, but He wanted us to have friendships with other people as well. Sometimes, it may seem easier to not bother with friendships. They can be frustrating and challenging and often painful. But the Bible specifically tells us that we were not meant to live without friendship. When our friendships are focused on God, we show the world how much Jesus loves us.

The devil is always trying to destroy our friendships. He tries his best to stir up trouble between friends and get you to gossip about the people you love. We'll learn about how to avoid unhealthy friendships and how to make sure we are good friends to others.

God has provided us with friends. He is our ultimate best friend, but we also need friendships with other people to help us grow in our walk with God and endure difficult times. Jesus is the perfect example of how to have friendships and show His love to the world. Our friendships will never be perfect, but we can encourage and build each other up, showing the world what it means to forgive and love one another.

READING PLAN

WEEK 1
OUR NEED FOR FRIENDSHIP

Monday: Designed for Friendship
Read: Genesis 1:26-27, 1 John 1:3
SOAP: Genesis 1:27

Tuesday: Created for Community
Read: Genesis 2:18, Ecclesiastes 4:9-12, Matthew 18:20
SOAP: Ecclesiastes 4:9-12

Wednesday: The Impact of Sin on Friendship
Read: Genesis 3:8-13, Genesis 4:6-8
SOAP: Genesis 3:8

Thursday: How Friendship Displays the Gospel
Read: John 13:35, 2 Corinthians 5:18-20
SOAP: John 13:35

Friday: Rooftop Ripping Friends
Read: Mark 2:1-5
SOAP: Mark 2:4

WEEK 2
WHAT IS BIBLICAL FRIENDSHIP?

Monday: Christ-Centered Friendship
Read: Romans 12:1-8, 1 Peter 4:10
SOAP: Romans 12:4-5, 1 Peter 4:10

Tuesday: The Purpose of Biblical Friendships
Read: John 17:20-24
SOAP: John 17:22-23

Wednesday: Thicker than Blood
Read: 1 Samuel 18:1-4, 1 Samuel 20
SOAP: 1 Samuel 18:1-4

Thursday: Lifting Each Other's Load
Read: Galatians 6:1-10
SOAP: Galatians 6:2

Friday: Support in a Broken World
Read: Hebrews 10:24-25, Ruth 1:16-17
SOAP: Hebrews 10:24-25

THE BLESSING OF FRIENDSHIP

Monday: The Golden Rule
Read: Luke 6:31-36
SOAP: Luke 6:31

Tuesday: Speak Truth in Love
Read: Proverbs 27:5-6, Proverbs 28:23, Ephesians 4:15-16
SOAP: Ephesians 4:15-16

Wednesday: A Friend Who is Trustworthy
Read: Proverbs 11:13
SOAP: Proverbs 11:13

Thursday: Friends Who Sharpen
Read: Proverbs 27:17, Proverbs 27:9
SOAP: Proverbs 27:17

Friday: The Need for Forgiveness
Read: Colossians 3:12-14, Ephesians 4:32, Proverbs 17:17
SOAP: Colossians 3:12-14

DANGEROUS FRIENDSHIPS

Monday: Counterfeit Friendships
Read: Proverbs 17:9, Romans 16:17-18, 2 Timothy 3:2-5
SOAP: Romans 16:17-18

Tuesday: Threats to Biblical Friendship
Read: Ephesians 6:12, Proverbs 11:9, Proverbs 11:13
SOAP: Ephesians 6:12

Wednesday: Red Flags
Read: Proverbs 22:24-25, Proverbs 27:4, 1 Corinthians 15:33, James 4:4-6
SOAP: James 4:4

Thursday: The Impact of Our Words
Read: Ephesians 4:29, Proverbs 16:24, Proverbs 16:28
SOAP: Ephesians 4:29

Friday: The Importance of Love
Read: 1 Corinthians 13, Proverbs 12:26
SOAP: 1 Corinthians 13:4-7

WEEK 5

JESUS, A FRIEND OF SINNERS

Monday: Jesus, Friend of Sinners
Read: John 8:1-11, 1 Timothy 1:15, Luke 5:31-32, Luke 7:34-35
SOAP: 1 Timothy 1:15

Tuesday: Outer Circle, Inner Circle
Read: Mark 3:13-19, Mark 5:37, Mark 9:2-8
SOAP: Mark 9:2

Wednesday: To Save the Lost
Read: Luke 15:1-10, Luke 19:1-10
SOAP: Luke 19:10

Thursday: Love Your Neighbor
Read: Mark 12:30-31, Galatians 5:14-17
SOAP: Galatians 5:14

Friday: Breaking Bread Together
Read: Acts 2:42-47, Acts 20:7
SOAP: Acts 2:46-47

WEEK 6

THE PROVISION OF FRIENDSHIP

Monday: Jesus, Our Ultimate Best Friend
Read: 1 Peter 5:6-7
SOAP: 1 Peter 5:7

Tuesday: He Calls You Friend
Read: John 15:14-17
SOAP: John 15:15

Wednesday: He is Our Faithful Friend
Read: Proverbs 18:24, Hebrews 13:5-6
SOAP: Proverbs 18:24

Thursday: The Ultimate Sacrifice
Read: John 15:13, Romans 5:8, Ephesians 5:1-2
SOAP: John 15:13

Friday: Life-Giving Friendships
Read: Philippians 2:1-18, Romans 12:9-21
SOAP: Romans 12:9-10

YOUR GOALS

We believe it's important to write out goals for this study. Take some time now and write three goals you would like to focus on as you begin to rise each day and dig into God's Word. Make sure and refer back to these goals throughout the next weeks to help you stay focused. You can do it!

1.

2.

3.

Signature:

Date:

PRAYER

WRITE DOWN YOUR PRAYER REQUESTS AND PRAISES FOR EACH DAY.

Prayer focus for this week:
Spend time praying for your family members.

MONDAY

TUESDAY

WEDNESDAY

THURSDAY

FRIDAY

WEEK 1
Our Need for Friendship

Everyone will know by this that you are my disciples—if you have love for one another.

John 13:35

SCRIPTURE FOR WEEK 1

MONDAY

Genesis 1:26-27

26 Then God said, "Let us make humankind in our image, after our likeness, so they may rule over the fish of the sea and the birds of the air, over the cattle, and over all the earth, and over all the creatures that move on the earth."

27 God created humankind in his own image,
in the image of God he created them,
male and female he created them.

1 John 1:3

3 What we have seen and heard we announce to you too, so that you may have fellowship with us (and indeed our fellowship is with the Father and with his Son Jesus Christ).

TUESDAY

Genesis 2:18

18 The LORD God said, "It is not good for the man to be alone. I will make a companion for him who corresponds to him."

Ecclesiastes 4:9-12

9 Two people are better than one,
because they can reap more benefit from their labor.
10 For if they fall, one will help his companion up,
but pity the person who falls down and has no one to help him up.
11 Furthermore, if two lie down together, they can keep each other warm,
but how can one person keep warm by himself?
12 Although an assailant may overpower one person,
two can withstand him.
Moreover, a three-stranded cord is not quickly broken.

Matthew 18:20

20 For where two or three are assembled in my name, I am there among them."

WEDNESDAY

Genesis 3:8-13

8 Then the man and his wife heard the sound of the Lord God moving about in the orchard at the breezy time of the day, and they hid from the Lord God among the trees of the orchard. 9 But the Lord God called to the man and said to him, "Where are you?" 10 The man replied, "I heard you moving about in the orchard, and I was afraid because I was naked, so I hid." 11 And the Lord God said, "Who told you that you were naked? Did you eat from the tree that I commanded you not to eat from?" 12 The man said, "The woman whom you gave me, she gave me some fruit from the tree and I ate it." 13 So the Lord God said to the woman, "What is this you have done?" And the woman replied, "The serpent tricked me, and I ate."

Genesis 4:6-8

6 Then the Lord said to Cain, "Why are you angry, and why is your expression downcast? 7 Is it not true that if you do what is right, you will be fine? But if you do not do what is right, sin is crouching at the door. It desires to dominate you, but you must subdue it."

8 Cain said to his brother Abel, "Let's go out to the field." While they were in the field, Cain attacked his brother Abel and killed him.

THURSDAY

John 13:35

35 Everyone will know by this that you are my disciples—if you have love for one another."

2 Corinthians 5:18-20

18 And all these things are from God who reconciled us to himself through Christ, and who has given us the ministry of reconciliation. 19 In other words, in Christ God was reconciling the world to himself, not counting people's trespasses against them, and he has given us the message of reconciliation. 20 Therefore we are ambassadors for Christ, as though God were making his plea through us. We plead with you on Christ's behalf, "Be reconciled to God!"

FRIDAY

Mark 2:1-5

Now after some days, when he returned to Capernaum, the news spread that he was at home. 2 So many gathered that there was no longer any room, not even by the door, and he preached the word to them. 3 Some people came bringing to him a paralytic, carried by four of them. 4 When they were not able to bring him in because of the crowd, they removed the roof above Jesus. Then, after tearing it out, they lowered the stretcher the paralytic was lying on. 5 When Jesus saw their faith, he said to the paralytic, "Son, your sins are forgiven."

MONDAY

Read:
Genesis 1:26-27, 1 John 1:3
SOAP:
Genesis 1:27

1. Write out today's **SCRIPTURE** passage.

_____

_____

_____

_____

_____

_____

_____

_____

_____

_____

2. On the blank page to the right, **DRAW** or **WRITE** what this passage means to you.

3. My **PRAYER** for today:

_____

_____

_____

_____

_____

TUESDAY

Read:
Genesis 2:18, Ecclesiastes 4:9-12, Matthew 18:20
SOAP:
Ecclesiastes 4:9-12

1. Write out today's **SCRIPTURE** passage.

_____

_____

_____

_____

_____

_____

_____

_____

_____

_____

2. On the blank page to the right, **DRAW** or **WRITE** what this passage means to you.

3. My **PRAYER** for today:

_____

_____

_____

_____

_____

WEDNESDAY

Read:
Genesis 3:8-13, Genesis 4:6-8
SOAP:
Genesis 3:8

1. Write out today's **SCRIPTURE** passage.

_____

_____

_____

_____

_____

_____

_____

_____

_____

_____

2. On the blank page to the right, **DRAW** or **WRITE** what this passage means to you.

3. My **PRAYER** for today:

_____

_____

_____

_____

_____

THURSDAY

Read:
John 13:35, 2 Corinthians 5:18-20
SOAP:
John 13:35

1. Write out today's **SCRIPTURE** passage.

_____

_____

_____

_____

_____

_____

_____

_____

_____

_____

2. On the blank page to the right, **DRAW** or **WRITE** what this passage means to you.

3. My **PRAYER** for today:

_____

_____

_____

_____

_____

_____

FRIDAY

Read:
Mark 2:1-5
SOAP:
Mark 2:4

1. Write out today's **SCRIPTURE** passage.

_____

_____

_____

_____

_____

_____

_____

_____

_____

_____

2. On the blank page to the right, **DRAW** or **WRITE** what this passage means to you.

3. My **PRAYER** for today:

_____

_____

_____

_____

_____

THIS WEEK I LEARNED...

USE THE SPACE BELOW TO DRAW A PICTURE OR WRITE ABOUT WHAT YOU LEARNED THIS WEEK FROM YOUR TIME IN GOD'S WORD.

THE AMAZING MAZE

FIND YOUR WAY THROUGH THE MAZE TO THE DIFFERENT
VERSES AND LOOK THEM UP IN YOUR BIBLE.

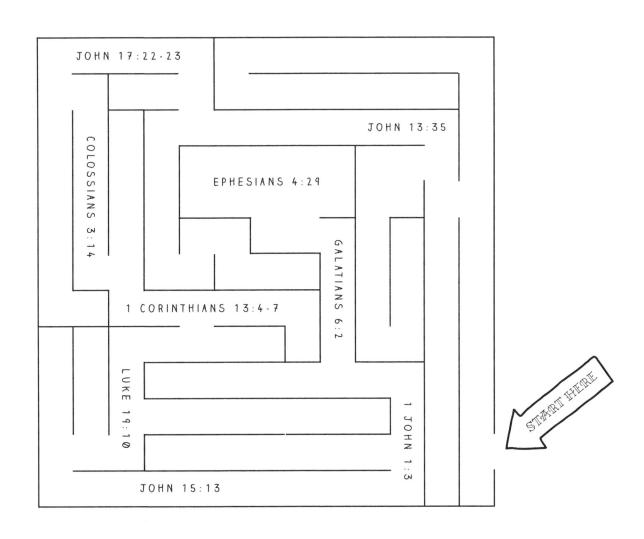

JOHN 17:22-23

JOHN 13:35

COLOSSIANS 3:14

EPHESIANS 4:29

GALATIANS 6:2

1 CORINTHIANS 13:4-7

LUKE 19:10

1 JOHN 1:3

START HERE

JOHN 15:13

PRAYER

WRITE DOWN YOUR PRAYER REQUESTS
AND PRAISES FOR EACH DAY.

Prayer focus for this week:
Spend time praying for your country.

MONDAY

TUESDAY

WEDNESDAY

THURSDAY

FRIDAY

WEEK 2
What is Biblical Friendship?

The glory you gave to me I have given to them, that they may be one just as we are one—I in them and you in me—that they may be completely one, so that the world will know that you sent me, and you have loved them just as you have loved me.

John 17:22-23

_____

SCRIPTURE FOR WEEK 2

MONDAY

Romans 12:1-8

Therefore I exhort you, brothers and sisters, by the mercies of God, to present your bodies as a sacrifice—alive, holy, and pleasing to God—which is your reasonable service. 2 Do not be conformed to this present world, but be transformed by the renewing of your mind, so that you may test and approve what is the will of God—what is good and well-pleasing and perfect.

3 For by the grace given to me I say to every one of you not to think more highly of yourself than you ought to think, but to think with sober discernment, as God has distributed to each of you a measure of faith. 4 For just as in one body we have many members, and not all the members serve the same function, 5 so we who are many are one body in Christ, and individually we are members who belong to one another. 6 And we have different gifts according to the grace given to us. If the gift is prophecy, that individual must use it in proportion to his faith. 7 If it is service, he must serve; if it is teaching, he must teach; 8 if it is exhortation, he must exhort; if it is contributing, he must do so with sincerity; if it is leadership, he must do so with diligence; if it is showing mercy, he must do so with cheerfulness.

1 Peter 4:10

10 Just as each one has received a gift, use it to serve one another as good stewards of the varied grace of God.

TUESDAY

John 17:20-24

20 "I am not praying only on their behalf, but also on behalf of those who believe in me through their testimony, 21 that they will all be one, just as you, Father, are in me and I am in you. I pray that they will be in us, so that the world will believe that you sent me. 22 The glory you gave to me I have given to them, that they may be one just as we are one— 23 I in them and you in me—that they may be completely one, so that the world will know that you sent me, and you have loved them just as you have loved me.

24 "Father, I want those you have given me to be with me where I am, so that they can see my glory that you gave me because you loved me before the creation of the world.

WEDNESDAY

1 Samuel 18:1-4

When David had finished talking with Saul, Jonathan and David became bound together in close friendship. Jonathan loved David as much as he did his own life. 2 Saul retained David on that day and did not allow him to return to his father's house. 3 Jonathan made a covenant with David, for he loved him as much as he did his own life. 4 Jonathan took off the robe he was wearing and gave it to David, along with the rest of his gear including his sword, his bow, and even his belt.

1 Samuel 20

David fled from Naioth in Ramah. He came to Jonathan and asked, "What have I done? What is my offense? How have I sinned before your father, that he is seeking my life?"

2 Jonathan said to him, "By no means are you going to die! My father does nothing large or small without making me aware of it. Why would my father hide this matter from me? It just won't happen!"

3 Taking an oath, David again said, "Your father is very much aware of the fact that I have found favor with you, and he has thought, 'Don't let Jonathan know about this, or he will be upset.' But as surely as the Lord lives and you live, there is about one step between me and death!" 4 Jonathan replied to David, "Tell me what I can do for you."

5 David said to Jonathan, "Tomorrow is the new moon, and I am certainly expected to join the king for a meal. You must send me away so I can hide in the field until the third evening from now. 6 If your father happens to miss me, you should say, 'David urgently requested me to let him go to his town Bethlehem, for there is an annual sacrifice there for his entire family.' 7 If he should then say, 'That's fine,' then your servant is safe. But if he becomes very angry, be assured that he has decided to harm me. 8 You must be loyal to your servant, for you have made a covenant with your servant in the Lord's name. If I am guilty, you yourself kill me! Why bother taking me to your father?"

9 Jonathan said, "Far be it from you to suggest this! If I were at all aware that my father had decided to harm you, wouldn't I tell you about it?" 10 David said to Jonathan, "Who will tell me if your father answers you harshly?" 11 Jonathan said to David, "Come on. Let's go out to the field."

When the two of them had gone out into the field, 12 Jonathan said to David, "The Lord God of Israel is my witness! I will feel out my father about this time the day after tomorrow. If he is favorably inclined toward David, will I not then send word to you and let you know? 13 But if my father intends to do you harm, may the Lord do all this and more to Jonathan, if I don't let you know and send word to you, so you can go safely on your way. May the Lord be with you, as he was with my father. 14 While I am still alive, extend to me the loyalty of the Lord, or else I will die. 15 Don't ever cut off your loyalty to my family, not even when the Lord has cut off every one of David's enemies from the face of the earth 16 and called David's enemies to account." So Jonathan made a covenant with the house of David. 17 Jonathan once again took an oath with David, because he loved him. In fact Jonathan loved him as much as he did his own life. 18 Jonathan said to him, "Tomorrow is the new moon, and you will be missed, for your seat will be empty. 19 On the third day you should go down quickly and come to the place where you hid yourself the day this all started. Stay near the stone Ezel. 20 I will shoot three arrows near it, as though I were shooting at a target. 21 When I send a boy after them, I will say, 'Go and find the arrows.' If I say to the boy, 'Look, the arrows are on this side of you; get them,' then come back. For as surely as the LORD lives, you will be safe and there will be no problem. 22 But if I say to the boy, 'Look, the arrows are on the other side of you,' then get away. For in that case the LORD has sent you away. 23 With regard to the matter that you and I discussed, the LORD is the witness between us forever."

24 So David hid in the field. When the new moon came, the king sat down to eat his meal. 25 The king sat down in his usual place by the wall, with Jonathan opposite him and Abner at his side. But David's place was vacant. 26 However, Saul said nothing about it that day, for he thought, "Something has happened to make him ceremonially unclean. Yes, he must be unclean." 27 But the next morning, the second day of the new moon, David's place was still vacant. So Saul said to his son Jonathan, "Why has Jesse's son not come to the meal yesterday or today?"

28 Jonathan replied to Saul, "David urgently requested that he be allowed to go to Bethlehem. 29 He said, 'Permit me to go, for we are having a family sacrifice in the town, and my brother urged me to be there. So now, if I have found favor with you, let me go to see my brothers.' For that reason he has not come to the king's table."

30 Saul became angry with Jonathan and said to him, "You stupid traitor! Don't I realize that to your own disgrace and to the disgrace of your mother's nakedness you have chosen this son of Jesse? 31 For as long as this son of Jesse is alive on the earth, you and your kingdom will not be established. Now, send some men and bring him to me. For he is as good as dead!"

32 Jonathan responded to his father Saul, "Why should he be put to death? What has he done?" 33 Then Saul threw his spear at Jonathan in order to strike him down. So Jonathan was convinced that his father had decided to kill David. 34 Jonathan got up from the table enraged. He did not eat any food on that second day of the new moon, for he was upset that his father had humiliated David.

35 The next morning Jonathan, along with a young servant, went out to the field to meet David. 36 He said to his servant, "Run, find the arrows that I am about to shoot." As the servant ran, Jonathan shot the arrow beyond him. 37 When the servant came to the place where Jonathan had shot the arrow, Jonathan called out to the servant, "Isn't the arrow farther beyond you?" 38 Jonathan called out to the servant, "Hurry! Go faster! Don't delay!" Jonathan's servant retrieved the arrow and came back to his master. 39 (Now the servant did not understand any of this. Only Jonathan and David knew what was going on.) 40 Then Jonathan gave his equipment to the servant who was with him. He said to him, "Go, take these things back to the town."

41 When the servant had left, David got up from beside the mound, knelt with his face to the ground, and bowed three times. Then they kissed each other and they both wept,

especially David. 42 Jonathan said to David, "Go in peace, for the two of us have sworn together in the name of the Lord saying, 'The Lord will be between me and you and between my descendants and your descendants forever.'"

THURSDAY

Galatians 6:1-10

Brothers and sisters, if a person is discovered in some sin, you who are spiritual restore such a person in a spirit of gentleness. Pay close attention to yourselves, so that you are not tempted too. 2 Carry one another's burdens, and in this way you will fulfill the law of Christ. 3 For if anyone thinks he is something when he is nothing, he deceives himself. 4 Let each one examine his own work. Then he can take pride in himself and not compare himself with someone else. 5 For each one will carry his own load.

6 Now the one who receives instruction in the word must share all good things with the one who teaches it. 7 Do not be deceived. God will not be made a fool. For a person will reap what he sows, 8 because the person who sows to his own flesh will reap corruption from the flesh, but the one who sows to the Spirit will reap eternal life from the Spirit. 9 So we must not grow weary in doing good, for in due time we will reap, if we do not give up. 10 So then, whenever we have an opportunity, let us do good to all people, and especially to those who belong to the family of faith.

FRIDAY

Hebrews 10:24-25

24 And let us take thought of how to spur one another on to love and good works, 25 not abandoning our own meetings, as some are in the habit of doing, but encouraging each other, and even more so because you see the day drawing near.

Ruth 1:16-17

16 But Ruth replied,
"Stop urging me to abandon you!
For wherever you go, I will go.
Wherever you live, I will live.
Your people will become my people,
and your God will become my God.
17 Wherever you die, I will die—and there I will be buried.
May the Lord punish me severely if I do not keep my promise!
Only death will be able to separate me from you!"

MONDAY

Read:
Romans 12:1-8, 1 Peter 4:10

SOAP:
Romans 12:4-5, 1 Peter 4:10

1. Write out today's **SCRIPTURE** passage.

_____

_____

_____

_____

_____

_____

_____

_____

_____

_____

2. On the blank page to the right, **DRAW** or **WRITE** what this passage means to you.

3. My **PRAYER** for today:

_____

_____

_____

_____

_____

TUESDAY

1. Write out today's **SCRIPTURE** passage.

_____

_____

_____

_____

_____

_____

_____

_____

_____

_____

2. On the blank page to the right, **DRAW** or **WRITE** what this passage means to you.

3. My **PRAYER** for today:

_____

_____

_____

_____

_____

WEDNESDAY

Read:
1 Samuel 18:1-4, 1 Samuel 20
SOAP:
1 Samuel 18:1-4

1. Write out today's **SCRIPTURE** passage.

_____

_____

_____

_____

_____

_____

_____

_____

_____

_____

2. On the blank page to the right, **DRAW** or **WRITE** what this passage means to you.

3. My **PRAYER** for today:

_____

_____

_____

_____

_____

THURSDAY

Read:
Galatians 6:1-10
SOAP:
Galatians 6:2

1. Write out today's **SCRIPTURE** passage.

_____

_____

_____

_____

_____

_____

_____

_____

_____

_____

2. On the blank page to the right, **DRAW** or **WRITE** what this passage means to you.

3. My **PRAYER** for today:

_____

_____

_____

_____

_____

FRIDAY

Read:
Hebrews 10:24-25, Ruth 1:16-17

SOAP:
Hebrews 10:24-25

1. Write out today's **SCRIPTURE** passage.

_____

_____

_____

_____

_____

_____

_____

_____

_____

_____

2. On the blank page to the right, **DRAW** or **WRITE** what this passage means to you.

3. My **PRAYER** for today:

_____

_____

_____

_____

_____

THIS WEEK I LEARNED...

USE THE SPACE BELOW TO DRAW A PICTURE OR WRITE ABOUT WHAT YOU LEARNED THIS WEEK FROM YOUR TIME IN GOD'S WORD.

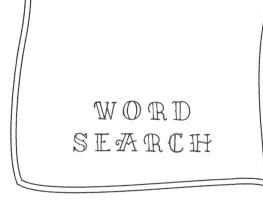

WORD SEARCH

SEARCH THROUGH THE WORD PUZZLE USING THE LIST OF WORDS BELOW.

FRIEND	SUPPORT	TRUST
JESUS	HELP	TRUTH
COMMUNITY	KINDNESS	FORGIVENESS
GOSPEL	LOVE	NEIGHBOR

```
F  H  N  F  V  D  X  S  O  K  Y  N  P  C  T  Z  I
N  Y  V  E  C  U  N  G  J  O  N  L  Y  B  W  C  I
Q  H  E  L  P  L  M  Y  I  S  K  Y  B  R  C  I  V
U  T  R  N  U  H  Y  F  F  R  I  E  N  D  P  L  E
T  R  U  S  T  T  Z  O  A  U  N  F  E  N  O  K  J
P  U  Y  N  L  V  U  R  E  H  D  X  I  V  F  D  E
N  T  Y  R  V  S  A  G  V  W  N  Q  G  O  M  N  S
L  H  B  T  V  S  U  I  Y  F  E  V  H  H  U  D  U
M  W  S  X  G  R  V  V  D  I  S  P  B  W  X  T  S
G  B  Q  S  Z  W  F  E  R  J  S  B  O  Y  K  I  N
O  E  C  O  M  M  U  N  I  T  Y  N  R  I  N  K  J
S  P  L  J  K  L  O  E  C  D  S  X  W  F  R  A  Q
P  G  T  V  F  G  D  S  H  Z  W  S  D  C  I  J  G
E  N  U  I  J  E  I  S  U  P  P  O  R  T  Y  J  U
L  O  V  E  J  F  R  D  V  S  X  Z  E  C  U  S  I
N  G  O  K  Y  N  T  F  R  G  P  L  W  D  T  G  S
```

PRAYER

WRITE DOWN YOUR PRAYER REQUESTS AND PRAISES FOR EACH DAY.

Prayer focus for this week:
Spend time praying for your friends.

MONDAY

TUESDAY

WEDNESDAY

THURSDAY

FRIDAY

WEEK 3
The Blessing of Friendship

And to all these virtues add love, which is the perfect bond.

Colossians 3:14

_____

SCRIPTURE FOR WEEK 3

MONDAY

Luke 6:31-36

31 Treat others in the same way that you would want them to treat you.

32 "If you love those who love you, what credit is that to you? For even sinners love those who love them. 33 And if you do good to those who do good to you, what credit is that to you? Even sinners do the same. 34 And if you lend to those from whom you hope to be repaid, what credit is that to you? Even sinners lend to sinners, so that they may be repaid in full. 35 But love your enemies, and do good, and lend, expecting nothing back. Then your reward will be great, and you will be sons of the Most High, because he is kind to ungrateful and evil people. 36 Be merciful, just as your Father is merciful.

TUESDAY

Proverbs 27:5-6

Better is open rebuke
than hidden love.
6 Faithful are the wounds of a friend,
but the kisses of an enemy are excessive.

Proverbs 28:23

The one who reproves another will in the end find more favor
than the one who flatters with the tongue.

Ephesians 4:15-16

15 But practicing the truth in love, we will in all things grow up into Christ, who is the head. 16 From him the whole body grows, fitted and held together through every supporting ligament. As each one does its part, the body builds itself up in love.

WEDNESDAY

Proverbs 11:13

The one who goes about slandering others reveals secrets,
but the one who is trustworthy conceals a matter.

THURSDAY

Proverbs 27:17

As iron sharpens iron,
so a person sharpens his friend.

Proverbs 27:9

Ointment and incense make the heart rejoice,
likewise the sweetness of one's friend from sincere counsel.

FRIDAY

Colossians 3:12-14

12 Therefore, as the elect of God, holy and dearly loved, clothe yourselves with a heart of mercy, kindness, humility, gentleness, and patience, 13 bearing with one another and forgiving one another, if someone happens to have a complaint against anyone else. Just as the Lord has forgiven you, so you also forgive others. 14 And to all these virtues add love, which is the perfect bond.

Ephesians 4:32

32 Instead, be kind to one another, compassionate, forgiving one another, just as God in Christ also forgave you.

Proverbs 17:17

A friend loves at all times,
and a relative is born to help in adversity.

MONDAY

Read:
Luke 6:31-36

SOAP:
Luke 6:31

1. Write out today's **SCRIPTURE** passage.

_____

_____

_____

_____

_____

_____

_____

_____

_____

_____

2. On the blank page to the right, **DRAW** or **WRITE** what this passage means to you.

3. My **PRAYER** for today:

_____

_____

_____

_____

_____

TUESDAY

Read:
Proverbs 27:5-6, Proverbs 28:23, Ephesians 4:15-16
SOAP:
Ephesians 4:15-16

1. Write out today's **SCRIPTURE** passage.

_____

_____

_____

_____

_____

_____

_____

_____

_____

_____

2. On the blank page to the right, **DRAW** or **WRITE** what this passage means to you.

3. My **PRAYER** for today:

_____

_____

_____

_____

_____

WEDNESDAY

1. Write out today's **SCRIPTURE** passage.

_____

_____

_____

_____

_____

_____

_____

_____

_____

_____

2. On the blank page to the right, **DRAW** or **WRITE** what this passage means to you.

3. My **PRAYER** for today:

_____

_____

_____

_____

_____

_____

THURSDAY

SOAP:
Proverbs 27:17

1. Write out today's **SCRIPTURE** passage.

_____

_____

_____

_____

_____

_____

_____

_____

_____

_____

2. On the blank page to the right, **DRAW** or **WRITE** what this passage means to you.

3. My **PRAYER** for today:

_____

_____

_____

_____

_____

FRIDAY

Read:
Colossians 3:12-14, Ephesians 4:32, Proverbs 17:17

SOAP:
Colossians 3:12-14

1. Write out today's SCRIPTURE passage.

_____

_____

_____

_____

_____

_____

_____

_____

_____

_____

2. On the blank page to the right, DRAW or WRITE what this passage means to you.

3. My PRAYER for today:

_____

_____

_____

_____

_____

THIS WEEK I LEARNED...

USE THE SPACE BELOW TO DRAW A PICTURE OR WRITE ABOUT WHAT YOU LEARNED THIS WEEK FROM YOUR TIME IN GOD'S WORD.

PRAYER TIME

IT'S IMPORTANT TO PRAY FOR OTHERS. WRITE A PRAYER
TO GOD FOR A FRIEND OR A FAMILY MEMBER.

....

....

....

....

....

....

....

....

....

....

....

....

PRAYER

WRITE DOWN YOUR PRAYER REQUESTS
AND PRAISES FOR EACH DAY.

Prayer focus for this week:
Spend time praying for your church.

MONDAY

TUESDAY

WEDNESDAY

THURSDAY

FRIDAY

WEEK 4
Dangerous Friendships

Love is patient, love is kind, it is not envious. Love does not brag, it is not puffed up. It is not rude, it is not self-serving, it is not easily angered or resentful. It is not glad about injustice, but rejoices in the truth. It bears all things, believes all things, hopes all things, endures all things.

1 Corinthians 13:4-7

SCRIPTURE FOR WEEK 4

MONDAY

Proverbs 17:9

The one who forgives an offense seeks love,
but whoever repeats a matter separates close friends.

Romans 16:17-18

17 Now I urge you, brothers and sisters, to watch out for those who create dissensions and obstacles contrary to the teaching that you learned. Avoid them! 18 For these are the kind who do not serve our LORD Christ, but their own appetites. By their smooth talk and flattery they deceive the minds of the naive.

2 Timothy 3:2-5

2 For people will be lovers of themselves, lovers of money, boastful, arrogant, blasphemers, disobedient to parents, ungrateful, unholy, 3 unloving, irreconcilable, slanderers, without self-control, savage, opposed to what is good, 4 treacherous, reckless, conceited, loving pleasure rather than loving God. 5 They will maintain the outward appearance of religion but will have repudiated its power. So avoid people like these.

TUESDAY

Ephesians 6:12

12 For our struggle is not against flesh and blood, but against the rulers, against the powers, against the world rulers of this darkness, against the spiritual forces of evil in the heavens.

Proverbs 11:9

With his speech the godless person destroys his neighbor,
but by knowledge the righteous will be delivered.

Proverbs 11:13

The one who goes about slandering others reveals secrets,
but the one who is trustworthy conceals a matter.

WEDNESDAY

Proverbs 22:24-25

Do not make friends with an angry person,
and do not associate with a wrathful person,
25 lest you learn his ways
and entangle yourself in a snare.

Proverbs 27:4

Wrath is cruel and anger is overwhelming,
but who can stand before jealousy?

1 Corinthians 15:33

33 Do not be deceived: "Bad company corrupts good morals."

James 4:4-6

4 Adulterers, do you not know that friendship with the world means hostility toward God? So whoever decides to be the world's friend makes himself God's enemy. 5 Or do you think the scripture means nothing when it says, "The spirit that God caused to live within us has an envious yearning"? 6 But he gives greater grace. Therefore it says, "**God opposes the proud, but he gives grace to the humble**."

THURSDAY

Ephesians 4:29

29 You must let no unwholesome word come out of your mouth, but only what is beneficial for the building up of the one in need, that it would give grace to those who hear.

Proverbs 16:24

Pleasant words are like a honeycomb,
sweet to the soul and healing to the bones.

Proverbs 16:28

A perverse person spreads dissension,
and a gossip separates the closest friends.

FRIDAY

1 Corinthians 13

If I speak in the tongues of men and of angels, but I do not have love, I am a noisy gong or a clanging cymbal. 2 And if I have prophecy, and know all mysteries and all knowledge, and if I have all faith so that I can remove mountains, but do not have love, I am nothing. 3 If I give away everything I own, and if I give over my body in order to boast, but do not have love, I receive no benefit.

4 Love is patient, love is kind, it is not envious. Love does not brag, it is not puffed up. 5 It is not rude, it is not self-serving, it is not easily angered or resentful. 6 It is not glad about injustice, but rejoices in the truth. 7 It bears all things, believes all things, hopes all things, endures all things.

8 Love never ends. But if there are prophecies, they will be set aside; if there are tongues, they will cease; if there is knowledge, it will be set aside. 9 For we know in part, and we prophesy in part, 10 but when what is perfect comes, the partial will be set aside. 11 When I was a child, I talked like a child, I thought like a child, I reasoned like a child. But when I became an adult, I set aside childish ways. 12 For now we see in a mirror indirectly, but then we will see face to face. Now I know in part, but then I will know fully, just as I have been fully known. 13 And now these three remain: faith, hope, and love. But the greatest of these is love.

Proverbs 12:26

The righteous person is cautious in his friendship,
but the way of the wicked leads them astray.

MONDAY

Read:
Proverbs 17:9, Romans 16:17-18, 2 Timothy 3:2-5

SOAP:
Romans 16:17-18

1. Write out today's **SCRIPTURE** passage.

_____

_____

_____

_____

_____

_____

_____

_____

_____

_____

2. On the blank page to the right, **DRAW** or **WRITE** what this passage means to you.

3. My **PRAYER** for today:

_____

_____

_____

_____

_____

_____

TUESDAY

Ephesians 6:12, Proverbs 11:9, Proverbs 11:13
SOAP:
Ephesians 6:12

1. Write out today's **SCRIPTURE** passage.

_____

_____

_____

_____

_____

_____

_____

_____

_____

_____

2. On the blank page to the right, **DRAW** or **WRITE** what this passage means to you.

3. My **PRAYER** for today:

_____

_____

_____

_____

_____

WEDNESDAY

1. Write out today's **SCRIPTURE** passage.

_____

_____

_____

_____

_____

_____

_____

_____

_____

2. On the blank page to the right, **DRAW** or **WRITE** what this passage means to you.

3. My **PRAYER** for today:

_____

_____

_____

_____

_____

_____

THURSDAY

Read:
Ephesians 4:29, Proverbs 16:24, Proverbs 16:28
SOAP:
Ephesians 4:29

1. Write out today's **SCRIPTURE** passage.

_____

_____

_____

_____

_____

_____

_____

_____

_____

_____

2. On the blank page to the right, **DRAW** or **WRITE** what this passage means to you.

3. My **PRAYER** for today:

_____

_____

_____

_____

_____

FRIDAY

Read:
1 Corinthians 13, Proverbs 12:26

SOAP:
1 Corinthians 13:4-7

1. Write out today's **SCRIPTURE** passage.

_____

_____

_____

_____

_____

_____

_____

_____

_____

_____

2. On the blank page to the right, **DRAW** or **WRITE** what this passage means to you.

3. My **PRAYER** for today:

_____

_____

_____

_____

_____

THIS WEEK I LEARNED...

USE THE SPACE BELOW TO DRAW A PICTURE OR WRITE ABOUT WHAT YOU LEARNED THIS WEEK FROM YOUR TIME IN GOD'S WORD.

FILL IN THE BLANK

READ THE VERSE AND USE IT TO FILL IN THE MISSING WORDS

Love is patient, love is kind, it is not envious. Love does not brag, it is not puffed up. It is not rude, it is not self-serving, it is not easily angered or resentful. It is not glad about injustice, but rejoices in the truth. It bears all things, believes all things, hopes all things, endures all things.

1 Corinthians 13:4-7

Love is _____, love is _____, it is not envious. Love does not brag, it is not puffed up. It is ____ rude, it is not self-serving, it is not _____ angered or resentful. It is not glad about injustice, but _____ in the _____. It bears all things, _____ all things, _____ all things, _____ all things.

PRAYER

WRITE DOWN YOUR PRAYER REQUESTS
AND PRAISES FOR EACH DAY.

Prayer focus for this week:
Spend time praying for your church.

MONDAY

TUESDAY

WEDNESDAY

THURSDAY

FRIDAY

WEEK 5
Jesus, a Friend of Sinners

For the Son of Man came to seek and to save the lost.

Luke 19:10

SCRIPTURE FOR WEEK 5

MONDAY

John 8:1-11

1 But Jesus went to the Mount of Olives. 2 Early in the morning he came to the temple courts again. All the people came to him, and he sat down and began to teach them. 3 The experts in the law and the Pharisees brought a woman who had been caught committing adultery. They made her stand in front of them 4 and said to Jesus, "Teacher, this woman was caught in the very act of adultery. 5 In the law *Moses commanded us to stone to death* such women. What then do you say?" 6 (Now they were asking this in an attempt to trap him, so that they could bring charges against him.) Jesus bent down and wrote on the ground with his finger. 7 When they persisted in asking him, he stood up straight and replied, "Whoever among you is guiltless may be the first to throw a stone at her." 8 Then he bent over again and wrote on the ground.

9 Now when they heard this, they began to drift away one at a time, starting with the older ones, until Jesus was left alone with the woman standing before him. 10 Jesus stood up straight and said to her, "Woman, where are they? Did no one condemn you?" 11 She replied, "No one, Lord." And Jesus said, "I do not condemn you either. Go, and from now on do not sin any more."

1 Timothy 1:15

15 This saying is trustworthy and deserves full acceptance: "Christ Jesus came into the world to save sinners"—and I am the worst of them!

Luke 5:31-32

31 Jesus answered them, "Those who are well don't need a physician, but those who are sick do. 32 I have not come to call the righteous, but sinners to repentance."

Luke 7:34-35

34 The Son of Man has come eating and drinking, and you say, 'Look at him, a glutton and a drunk, a friend of tax collectors and sinners!' 35 But wisdom is vindicated by all her children."

TUESDAY

Mark 3:13-19

13 Now Jesus went up the mountain and called for those he wanted, and they came to him. 14 He appointed twelve so that they would be with him and he could send them to preach 15 and to have authority to cast out demons. 16 To Simon he gave the name Peter; 17 to James and his brother John, the sons of Zebedee, he gave the name Boanerges (that is, "sons of thunder"); 18 and Andrew, Philip, Bartholomew, Matthew, Thomas, James the son of Alphaeus, Thaddaeus, Simon the Zealot, 19 and Judas Iscariot, who betrayed him.

Mark 5:37

37 He did not let anyone follow him except Peter, James, and John, the brother of James.

Mark 9:2-8

2 Six days later Jesus took with him Peter, James, and John and led them alone up a high mountain privately. And he was transfigured before them, 3 and his clothes became radiantly white, more so than any launderer in the world could bleach them. 4 Then Elijah appeared before them along with Moses, and they were talking with Jesus. 5 So Peter said to Jesus, "Rabbi, it is good for us to be here. Let us make three shelters—one for you, one for Moses, and one for Elijah." 6 (For they were afraid, and he did not know what to say.) 7 Then a cloud overshadowed them, and a voice came from the cloud, "This is my one dear Son. Listen to him!" 8 Suddenly when they looked around, they saw no one with them any more except Jesus.

WEDNESDAY

Luke 15:1-10

Now all the tax collectors and sinners were coming to hear him. 2 But the Pharisees and the experts in the law were complaining, "This man welcomes sinners and eats with them."

3 So Jesus told them this parable: 4 "Which one of you, if he has a hundred sheep and loses one of them, would not leave the ninety-nine in the open pasture and go look for the one that is lost until he finds it? 5 Then when he has found it, he places it on his shoulders, rejoicing. 6 Returning home, he calls together his friends and neighbors, telling them, 'Rejoice with me, because I have found my sheep that was lost.' 7 I tell you, in the same way there will be more joy in heaven over one sinner who repents than over ninety-nine righteous people who have no need to repent.

8 "Or what woman, if she has ten silver coins and loses one of them, does not light a lamp, sweep the house, and search thoroughly until she finds it? 9 Then when she has found it, she calls together her friends and neighbors, saying, 'Rejoice with me, for I have found the

coin that I had lost.' 10 In the same way, I tell you, there is joy in the presence of God's angels over one sinner who repents."

Luke 19:1-10

Jesus entered Jericho and was passing through it. 2 Now a man named Zacchaeus was there; he was a chief tax collector and was rich. 3 He was trying to get a look at Jesus, but being a short man he could not see over the crowd. 4 So he ran on ahead and climbed up into a sycamore tree to see him, because Jesus was going to pass that way. 5 And when Jesus came to that place, he looked up and said to him, "Zacchaeus, come down quickly, because I must stay at your house today." 6 So he came down quickly and welcomed Jesus joyfully. 7 And when the people saw it, they all complained, "He has gone in to be the guest of a man who is a sinner." 8 But Zacchaeus stopped and said to the LORD, "Look, LORD, half of my possessions I now give to the poor, and if I have cheated anyone of anything, I am paying back four times as much!" 9 Then Jesus said to him, "Today salvation has come to this household, because he too is a son of Abraham! 10 For the Son of Man came to seek and to save the lost."

THURSDAY

Mark 12:30-31

Love the LORD your God with all your heart, with all your soul, with all your mind, and with all your strength.' 31 The second is: '**Love your neighbor as yourself.**' There is no other commandment greater than these."

Galatians 5:14-17

14 For the whole law can be summed up in a single commandment, namely, "**You must love your neighbor as yourself.**" 15 However, if you continually bite and devour one another, beware that you are not consumed by one another. 16 But I say, live by the Spirit and you will not carry out the desires of the flesh. 17 For the flesh has desires that are opposed to the Spirit, and the Spirit has desires that are opposed to the flesh, for these are in opposition to each other, so that you cannot do what you want.

FRIDAY

Acts 2:42-47

42 They were devoting themselves to the apostles' teaching and to fellowship, to the breaking of bread and to prayer. 43 Reverential awe came over everyone, and many wonders and miraculous signs came about by the apostles. 44 All who believed were together and held everything in common, 45 and they began selling their property and possessions and

distributing the proceeds to everyone, as anyone had need. 46 Every day they continued to gather together by common consent in the temple courts, breaking bread from house to house, sharing their food with glad and humble hearts, 47 praising God and having the good will of all the people. And the LORD was adding to their number every day those who were being saved.

Acts 20:7

7 On the first day of the week, when we met to break bread, Paul began to speak to the people, and because he intended to leave the next day, he extended his message until midnight.

MONDAY

Read:
John 8:1-11, 1 Timothy 1:15, Luke 5:31-32, Luke 7:34-35

SOAP:
1 Timothy 1:15

1. Write out today's **SCRIPTURE** passage.

_____

_____

_____

_____

_____

_____

_____

_____

_____

_____

2. On the blank page to the right, **DRAW** or **WRITE** what this passage means to you.

3. My **PRAYER** for today:

_____

_____

_____

_____

_____

TUESDAY

Read:
Mark 3:13-19, Mark 5:37, Mark 9:2-8
SOAP:
Mark 9:2

1. Write out today's **SCRIPTURE** passage.

_____

_____

_____

_____

_____

_____

_____

_____

_____

_____

2. On the blank page to the right, **DRAW** or **WRITE** what this passage means to you.

3. My **PRAYER** for today:

_____

_____

_____

_____

_____

WEDNESDAY

Read:
Luke 15:1-10, Luke 19:1-10
SOAP:
Luke 19:10

1. Write out today's **SCRIPTURE** passage.

_____

_____

_____

_____

_____

_____

_____

_____

_____

_____

2. On the blank page to the right, **DRAW** or **WRITE** what this passage means to you.

3. My **PRAYER** for today:

_____

_____

_____

_____

_____

99

THURSDAY

Read:
Mark 12:30-31, Galatians 5:14-17

SOAP:
Galatians 5:14

1. Write out today's **SCRIPTURE** passage.

_____

_____

_____

_____

_____

_____

_____

_____

_____

_____

2. On the blank page to the right, **DRAW** or **WRITE** what this passage means to you.

3. My **PRAYER** for today:

_____

_____

_____

_____

_____

FRIDAY

Read:
Acts 2:42-47, Acts 20:7

SOAP:
Acts 2:46-47

1. Write out today's **SCRIPTURE** passage.

_____

_____

_____

_____

_____

_____

_____

_____

_____

_____

2. On the blank page to the right, **DRAW** or **WRITE** what this passage means to you.

3. My **PRAYER** for today:

_____

_____

_____

_____

_____

THIS WEEK I LEARNED...

USE THE SPACE BELOW TO DRAW A PICTURE OR WRITE ABOUT WHAT YOU LEARNED THIS WEEK FROM YOUR TIME IN GOD'S WORD.

BIBLICAL FRIENDSHIP

WHAT ARE SOME WAYS YOU CAN SHOW LOVE TO YOUR FRIENDS THIS WEEK? WRITE DOWN A FEW IDEAS FOR EACH DAY:

MONDAY:
_____
_____

TUESDAY:
_____
_____

WEDNESDAY:
_____
_____

THURSDAY:
_____
_____

FRIDAY:
_____
_____

PRAYER

WRITE DOWN YOUR PRAYER REQUESTS AND PRAISES FOR EACH DAY.

Prayer focus for this week:
Spend time praying for your church.

MONDAY

TUESDAY

WEDNESDAY

THURSDAY

FRIDAY

WEEK 6
The Provision of Friendship

No one has greater love than
this—that one lays down
his life for his friends.

John 15:13

_____

SCRIPTURE FOR WEEK 6

MONDAY

1 Peter 5:6-7

6 And God will exalt you in due time, if you humble yourselves under his mighty hand 7 by casting all your cares on him because he cares for you.

TUESDAY

John 15:14-17

14 You are my friends if you do what I command you. 15 I no longer call you slaves, because the slave does not understand what his master is doing. But I have called you friends, because I have revealed to you everything I heard from my Father. 16 You did not choose me, but I chose you and appointed you to go and bear fruit, fruit that remains, so that whatever you ask the Father in my name he will give you. 17 This I command you—to love one another.

WEDNESDAY

Proverbs 18:24

There are companions who harm one another,
but there is a friend who sticks closer than a brother.

Hebrews 13:5-6

5 Your conduct must be free from the love of money and you must be content with what you have, for he has said, "***I will never leave you and I will never abandon you.***" 6 So we can say with confidence, "***The Lord is my helper, and I will not be afraid. What can people do to me?***"

THURSDAY

John 15:13

13 No one has greater love than this—that one lays down his life for his friends.

Romans 5:8

8 But God demonstrates his own love for us, in that while we were still sinners, Christ died for us.

Ephesians 5:1-2

Therefore, be imitators of God as dearly loved children 2 and live in love, just as Christ also loved us and gave himself for us, a sacrificial and fragrant offering to God.

FRIDAY

Philippians 2:1-18

Therefore, if there is any encouragement in Christ, any comfort provided by love, any fellowship in the Spirit, any affection or mercy, 2 complete my joy and be of the same mind, by having the same love, being united in spirit, and having one purpose. 3 Instead of being motivated by selfish ambition or vanity, each of you should, in humility, be moved to treat one another as more important than yourself. 4 Each of you should be concerned not only about your own interests, but about the interests of others as well. 5 You should have the same attitude toward one another that Christ Jesus had,

6 who though he existed in the form of God
did not regard equality with God
as something to be grasped,
7 but emptied himself
by taking on the form of a slave,
by looking like other men,
and by sharing in human nature.
8 He humbled himself,
by becoming obedient to the point of death
—even death on a cross!
9 As a result God highly exalted him
and gave him the name
that is above every name,
10 so that at the name of Jesus
every knee will bow
—in heaven and on earth and under the earth—
11 and every tongue confess
that Jesus Christ is LORD
to the glory of God the Father.

12 So then, my dear friends, just as you have always obeyed, not only in my presence but even more in my absence, continue working out your salvation with awe and

reverence, 13 for the one bringing forth in you both the desire and the effort—for the sake of his good pleasure—is God. 14 Do everything without grumbling or arguing, 15 so that you may be blameless and pure, children of God without blemish though you live in a crooked and perverse society, in which you shine as lights in the world 16 by holding on to the word of life so that on the day of Christ I will have a reason to boast that I did not run in vain nor labor in vain. 17 But even if I am being poured out like a drink offering on the sacrifice and service of your faith, I am glad and rejoice together with all of you. 18 And in the same way you also should be glad and rejoice together with me.

Romans 12:9-21

9 Love must be without hypocrisy. Abhor what is evil, cling to what is good. 10 Be devoted to one another with mutual love, showing eagerness in honoring one another. 11 Do not lag in zeal, be enthusiastic in spirit, serve the Lord. 12 Rejoice in hope, endure in suffering, persist in prayer. 13 Contribute to the needs of the saints, pursue hospitality. 14 Bless those who persecute you, bless and do not curse. 15 Rejoice with those who rejoice, weep with those who weep. 16 Live in harmony with one another; do not be haughty but associate with the lowly. Do not be conceited. 17 Do not repay anyone evil for evil; consider what is good before all people. 18 If possible, so far as it depends on you, live peaceably with all people. 19 Do not avenge yourselves, dear friends, but give place to God's wrath, for it is written, "*Vengeance is mine, I will repay*," says the Lord. 20 Rather, *if your enemy is hungry, feed him; if he is thirsty, give him a drink; for in doing this you will be heaping burning coals on his head*. 21 Do not be overcome by evil, but overcome evil with good.

MONDAY

1. Write out today's **SCRIPTURE** passage.

_____

_____

_____

_____

_____

_____

_____

_____

_____

2. On the blank page to the right, **DRAW** or **WRITE** what this passage means to you.

3. My **PRAYER** for today:

_____

_____

_____

_____

_____

TUESDAY

Read:
John 15:14-17
SOAP:
John 15:15

1. Write out today's **SCRIPTURE** passage.

_____

_____

_____

_____

_____

_____

_____

_____

2. On the blank page to the right, **DRAW** or **WRITE** what this passage means to you.

3. My **PRAYER** for today:

_____

_____

_____

_____

_____

WEDNESDAY

Proverbs 18:24, Hebrews 13:5-6

SOAP:
Proverbs 18:24

1. Write out today's **SCRIPTURE** passage.

_____

_____

_____

_____

_____

_____

_____

_____

_____

_____

2. On the blank page to the right, **DRAW** or **WRITE** what this passage means to you.

3. My **PRAYER** for today:

_____

_____

_____

_____

_____

THURSDAY

Read:
John 15:13, Romans 5:8, Ephesians 5:1-2
SOAP:
John 15:13

1. Write out today's **SCRIPTURE** passage.

_____

_____

_____

_____

_____

_____

_____

_____

_____

_____

2. On the blank page to the right, **DRAW** or **WRITE** what this passage means to you.

3. My **PRAYER** for today:

_____

_____

_____

_____

_____

121

FRIDAY

Read:
Philippians 2:1-18, Romans 12:9-21
SOAP:
Romans 12:9-10

1. Write out today's **SCRIPTURE** passage.

_____

_____

_____

_____

_____

_____

_____

_____

_____

_____

2. On the blank page to the right, **DRAW** or **WRITE** what this passage means to you.

3. My **PRAYER** for today:

_____

_____

_____

_____

_____

THIS WEEK I LEARNED...

USE THE SPACE BELOW TO DRAW A PICTURE OR WRITE ABOUT WHAT YOU LEARNED THIS WEEK FROM YOUR TIME IN GOD'S WORD.

SHARE WITH A FRIEND:

This last activity page is meant to be shared! Cut out the following page. Write a letter to a friend on the front, and decorate the envelope on the back. Fold, seal with a sticker, and deliver!

Feel free to make copies of the envelope page to give to more than one friend!

Made in the USA
Columbia, SC
14 November 2021

48954120R00076